HOUGHTON MIFFLIN
Reading
A Legacy of Literacy

Family Time

HOUGHTON MIFFLIN

BOSTON • MORRIS PLAINS, NJ

California • Colorado • Georgia • Illinois • New Jersey • Texas

Printed in the U.S.A.

ISBN 0-618-07506-2

3456789-BS-05 04 03 02 01 00

Design, Art Management, and Page Production: Silver Editions.

Contents

My Sister Joan

by Becky Ward
illustrated by John Bendall-Brunello

My name is Kevin but my sister calls
me Buster. Her name is Joan.

It seems like trouble can find Joan no
matter where she is.

1

When Joan gets in a jam and needs
help, she yells for me.

Last summer we went swimming at
the lake. Joan ran around trying to
catch grasshoppers. She never expected
to get stung by a bee!

"OUCH! Buster! Get that bad grasshopper!" yelled Joan.

I rubbed butter on her hand and explained to her about bees and stingers.

Another time we ate ice cream at
Uncle Frank's house. When Joan tried to
go outside, she let Uncle Frank's dog in.
Joan yelled, "Buster! It's my ice cream.
Help!"

I ran in. There was Joan with ice
cream melting down her arm and a dog
licking her face.

4

Last night, Mom and Dad went to a dinner party. I let the babysitter know that she must keep a close eye on Joan.

"We had better check on her," I said.

Then it happened. After a loud crash, Joan hollered, "Buster! Quick! I didn't mean to do it."

We ran and found Joan standing in the middle of the bedroom in a pool of perfume.

The sitter cleaned up the glass, and I wiped up the perfume with water. Joan took a bath, but she still smelled awful.

6

Big brothers must help younger
sisters, so I tried to make Joan
understand that she needed to stay
away from trouble.

"What trouble, Buster?" she asked,
as she gave me a big grape jelly hug.

The Big Party Plan

by Becky Ward
illustrated by Elizabeth Wolf

"Children, get your coats on. We're going shopping in Willow Creek!" Mother called.

"Shopping? Willow Creek? Us?" The children thought Mother might be kidding. The Chang family lived on a farm and hardly ever went to Willow Creek, a town forty miles away.

"Yes, we're going shopping," said
Mother. "Did you forget that we're
throwing a party? We will get party
food and other things that we'll need.
I will let you do your own shopping
for gifts."

"Hooray!" cried the children,
running to get coats and snow boots.

At Mister Sloan's store, the Changs
roamed up and down the rows
looking for gifts. Ann chose three
sweet-smelling bars of soap. Chester
found some yellow slippers. Joan
picked out peppermint bath oil that
would be nice to soak in. Paul got
garden seeds for growing flowers.

"Those are nice choices," said Mother.

Mother got a pot roast, salad greens, cake mix, streamers, and balloons. They loaded everything up and started for home. Shopping put them in a happy mood, so they sang a few happy tunes as they drove down the snowy road.

When they got home, Mother said, "Let's get started. We've got loads to get done."

Mother had Paul and Joan blow up balloons. Then they hung streamers and a big "Happy Birthday" banner. Ann baked a yellow cake and Chester made a bowl of white frosting. Then the children wrapped gifts and made cards.

The next day, Father's red pickup
truck came slowly up the driveway.
Father and Grandmother got out.
They had made a long trip in the snow.
The children ran and greeted them on
the steps.

"Grandmother, we've got something
to show you!" cried Joan.

14

Joan led Grandmother to the other room.

"Happy Birthday!" everyone shouted.

When Grandmother saw the banner, cake, and gifts, she hugged everyone. Then she laughed and said, "This family really knows how to throw a party!"

Lost and Found

by Anne Walker
illustrated by Devin Hunt

Lee woke up early. He looked in the
red box under his bed.

Sparkle, his black and white cat, had
not slept there. She had been missing
for three days and nights.

"We'll just have to keep looking,"
Lee mumbled.

Nan and Fran came in. Fran was
munching an apple.

"Lee," Nan said. "Can you help us?
We don't know where we put our
new pens."

"Yes, I can," replied Lee. "Then you
can help me look for Sparkle."

Nan, Fran, and Lee went upstairs to find the pens.

They looked on Nan's desk. They looked under Fran's bed. They even looked in the wastebasket.

"Let's ask Mom," Lee said. "She'll know where we can look."

Then Lee looked at Fran and Nan.
A smile broke out on his face. He
started laughing.

"They'll never believe this," he
thought.

"What's making you laugh so hard?"
they asked. "Stop it!"

But Lee couldn't help himself.

At last Lee said, "Your pens are in your hair!"

Nan fumbled in her hair and found her pen. Then Fran found her pen in her curls.

"Pens instead of bows," Nan said with a chuckle. "We're going to start a new trend!"

Next, Fran, Nan, and Lee started
to hunt for Sparkle. Lee looked in
the kitchen.

Nan looked around the couch.
"Lee! Fran! Come here!" she shouted.

"Look at that," Lee said softly.
"Sparkle's got six brand new kittens!"

They looked at Sparkle's kittens.
Three black kittens slept. Three white
kittens stumbled on Sparkle's tail.

"Good job, Nan," he said. "I wouldn't
have found Sparkle without your help."

What Will Lester Be?

by Anne Walker

illustrated by April Hartmann

Lester's dad handed him a dinner plate. Lester dried it with a red cloth. He set it on the counter.

"Dad, what will I be when I grow up?" he asked quietly.

25

"You like cooking," Dad replied.

"Yes," Lester said. "I can make crust for pies. And I know how to use a roller." He stopped to think.

"That's it! I might be a baker," Lester shouted with joy.

On Thursday, Lester threw three
fast pitches. Ron missed them.

"I can throw fast!" Lester thought.
"That's it! I might be a pitcher for
big teams."

When Lester went hiking with his big sister, she said, "You might be a teacher like Miss Tuggle."

"Yes," Lester replied. "I could keep rulers, paper, and pens in my desk." Then he cried, "That's it! I might be a teacher!"

That afternoon, Lester looked at a book. His grandmother sat with him. "You like reading," she said.

"That's right," Lester replied. "I like reading and telling stories." He stopped to think.

"I might be a writer!" Lester exclaimed.

"You might be many things," said his grandmother.

"That's right!" exclaimed Lester. "I can cook, throw fast, read, and tell stories! I can be a lot of things when I grow up."

"You are something right now,
Lester," Grandmother said. "You are
the best grandson in the world. So try
not to grow up too fast," she said with
a smile.

Aunt Lizzy Finds Her Cake

by Patty Moynahan
illustrated by Margeaux Lucas

Just look at this messy table! Willy and Pam are making a cake for Aunt Lizzy. Today is her birthday. This cake will be unlike other cakes. Aunt Lizzy must find this cake first. Then she can eat it!

Pam is writing notes with funny
clues. Aunt Lizzy must read each clue
to get her cake.

"Look inside a green fuzzy thing,"
reads the first clue. "Untie the string
and read the note."

Aunt Lizzy is looking for her cake.
Her first clue was in a pair of slippers.

"Hurry!" urged the next note. "Go
where flowers grow. It is unwise to
waste time."

Aunt Lizzy rushed outside. Willy
and Pam followed her.

"Go up three steps. A gift is waiting for you. Unwrap this gift and look inside."

36

Willy and Pam looked at each other
and smiled. Aunt Lizzy found her last
clue.

"Go where cars sleep. Look for a big
white box."

Aunt Lizzy found her cake. Benny
had found the cake first. He did not
need to read clues. Willy looked at Pam.

"I unlocked Benny's pen and forgot to
lock it again."

Everyone went inside and ate ice cream and cookies.

"I would not take a million dollars for this day," said Aunt Lizzy. "Thanks for my birthday surprise."

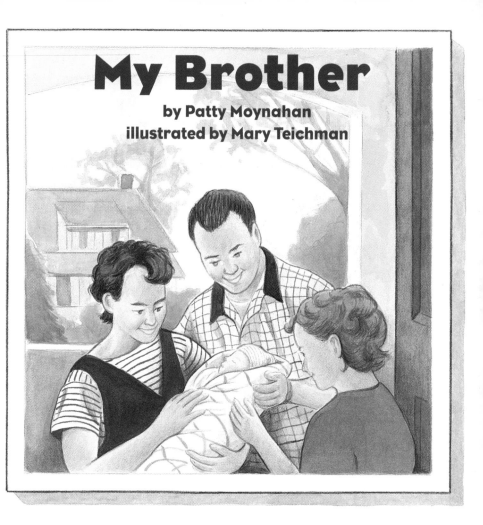

My Brother

by Patty Moynahan
illustrated by Mary Teichman

Jack Comes Home

Mom and Dad are home at last!
"What is in the bundle, Mom?"

"This is your new brother," she tells
me. "His name is Jack."

41

My new brother looks so little.
"Can I hold him, Dad? I'll be gentle."

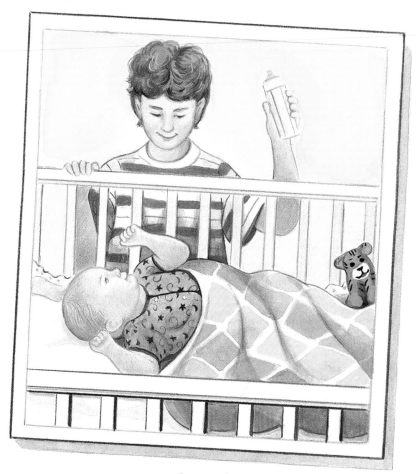

Jack Is One

What is Jack thinking? Why does he wiggle? "Jack, hurry up and talk. Hurry up and walk."

Jack sees this bottle. Jack makes me giggle.

Jack Is Two

Jack is playing with his rattle. "Jack, where are your manners? Don't play at the table. Eat your scrambled eggs and apple!"

44

Mom lets me give Jack a bath. Jack likes to play with bubbles. "Jack! Quit splashing me!"

"Time to get out now. Or else you will wrinkle."

Jack Is Three

We settle down for bed. "Will you read me this story?" asks Jack. This story is about an eagle. One day, I will teach my brother how to read.

We go for walks. I hold Jack's hand.
Jack is safe with me. We are brothers.
We are best friends.

Eight Daughters!

by Linda Dunlap
illustrated by Tamara Petrosino

In the Knox family there were eight daughters. Sissy Knox, at age fifteen, bossed them all around. She thought she knew just about everything! In fact, Sissy did know some things. She taught her younger sisters how to play right.

Then came the triplets — Peggy,
Meggy, and Bessy. Peggy dressed like
Meggy. Meggy dressed like Bessy. Bessy
dressed like Peggy. Not even Dad knew
which was which!

Child number five was Doreen.
Doreen liked baking. She made muffins
for the family. She kneaded and patted
each morning. Then she baked and
baked. Good smells filled the air. At
night, the Knox family ate fresh muffins
for dinner.

Myra, the sixth daughter, played drums. Neighbors held their heads every hour that Myra played. She knew how to keep a beat. But she played each tune with all her might. Her loud drumming made it hard to sleep at night.

Daughter number seven was Kate.
Kate had a knack for getting in scrapes.
She fell from tree limbs, skinning her
knees. Her clothes, hands, and face
were mainly muddy. Poor Kate always
looked a sight!

Little Sara, number eight, was not very heavy yet. Sara crawled through the house on her knees. She gave bright smiles to each person. Kneel to play with Sara, and you might get a tight hug.

Now you know about the eight Knox
daughters. Next time I might tell you
about the eight Knox sons!

The Family Garden

by Linda Dunlap
illustrated by Linda Pierce

Each spring, Anna's family plants a garden. Everyone in her family helps.

57

Daddy plows the soil. His sure hands
make nice, straight rows. It is good that
Daddy is big. Plowing takes plenty of
energy!

Mom and Granny plant seeds. Each
seed is placed gently in the soil. Then
the seeds are topped with more soil.
Most rows get seventy seeds. Planting
can be hard work!

Finally, it is the children's turn. Anna and her brother make sure plants get what they need. They water the seedlings each day. They pull weeds, which take plants' food and air. Growing plants need air, sun, water, and food.

After many weeks, the garden is
finally in bloom. It takes a long time,
but plants need that much time to grow.
You cannot hurry plants.

Then harvest starts! Anna's family
spends sunny days picking good things
to eat. Harvest baskets get packed and
heavy. Everyone is thirsty, dirty, and
happy.

Now comes the best part! It is time
to enjoy all that work! Anna's happy
family eats many garden foods for
dinner. Then Granny surprises them
with fresh strawberry pie. You can see
why gardening is such fun!

Word Lists

Theme 5

My Sister Joan (p. 1) accompanies *Brothers and Sisters.*

Decodable Words

New

The -er Ending in Two-Syllable Words: after, better, brothers, Buster, butter, dinner, grasshopper, grasshoppers, hollered, matter, never, sister, sisters, sitter, stingers, summer, understand

Previously Taught

and, arm, around, as, asked, at, ate, away, awful, bad, bath, bedroom, bee, bees, big, by, but, came, can, catch, check, cleaned, close, crash, cream, Dad, didn't, dog, down, expected, explained, face, find, for, found, Frank's, from, gave, get, gets, glass, go, grape, had, hand, happened, help, her, house, hug, ice, in, is, it, it's, jam, Joan, jelly, keep, Kevin, know, lake, last, let, licking, loud, make, me, mean, melting, Mom, must, my, name, needed, needs, night, no, not, on, ouch, outside, party, perfume, pool, quick, ran, rubbed, seems, she, smelled, so, standing, stay, still, stung, swimming, that, then, time, took, tried, trying, up, we, went, when, wiped, with, yelled, yells

High-Frequency Words

New

middle, trouble, uncle

Previously Taught

a, about, another, baby, calls, do, eye, I, like, of, said, the, there, to, was, water, what, where, younger

The Big Party Plan (p. 9) accompanies *Brothers and Sisters.*

Decodable Words

Review

Vowel Pairs oa, ow: coats, Joan, loaded, loads, road, roamed, roast, Sloan's, soak, soap, blow, bowl, flowers, growing, knows, own, rows, show, slowly, snow, snowy, throw, throwing, willow, yellow

Previously Taught

and, Ann, as, at, away, baked, balloons, banner, bars, bath, be, big, birthday, boots, cake, came, cards, Chang, Changs, Chester, children, choices, chose, Creek, cried, day, did, down, driveway, drove, ever, family, farm, father, father's, few, food, for, forget, forty,

found, frosting, garden, get, gifts, going, got, grandmother, greens,
greeted, had, happy, hardly, home, hooray, how, hugged, hung, in,
kidding, led, let, let's, long, looking, made, might, miles, Mister, mix,
mood, mother, need, nice, oil, on, out, own, party, Paul, peppermint,
picked, pick-up, plan, pot, ran, really, room, running, salad, sang,
saw, seeds, she, shopping, shouted, slippers, smelling, so, started,
steps, store, streamers, sweet, that, them, then, things, this, those,
three, town, trip, truck, tunes, up, us, we'll, we're, we've, went,
when, white, will, wrapped, yes, you

High-Frequency Words
Previously Taught
a, are, called, do, done, everyone, everything, I, laughed, lived, of,
other, put, said, some, something, the, they, thought, to, would, your

Lost and Found (p. 17) accompanies *Jalapeño Bagels.*

Decodable Words
New
Structural Analysis: Contractions: *let's, she'll, Sparkle's, we'll, we're*
The *-le* Ending in Two-Syllable Words: *apple, chuckle, fumbled,*
mumbled, Sparkle, stumbled

Previously Taught
an, and, ask, asked, at, bed, black, bows, box, brand, broke, but,
came, can, cat, couch, curls, days, desk, face, find, five, for, found,
Fran, Fran's, good, going, got, had, hard, have, he, help, her, him-
self, his, hunt, in, it, job, just, keep, kittens, know, last, Lee, look,
looked, looking, making, me, missing, Mom, munching, Nan, Nan's,
never, new, next, nights, not, on, out, pen, pens, put, red, replied,
she, shouted, six, slept, smile, so, softly, start, started, stop, tail,
that, then, this, three, trend, under, up, upstairs, us, wastebasket,
we, went, white, with, without, woke, yes, you

High-Frequency Words
New
early, hair, instead

Previously Taught
a, are, around, been, believe, come, couldn't, don't, even, here, I,
kitchen, laugh, laughing, of, our, said, the, there, they, they'll,
thought, to, was, what's, where, wouldn't, your

What Will Lester Be? (p. 25) accompanies *Jalapeño Bagels.*

Decodable Words

Review
The -er Ending in Two-Syllable Words: *baker, counter, dinner, grandmother, Lester, Lester's, paper, pitcher, roller, rulers, sister, teacher, writer, water*

Previously Taught
afternoon, and, asked, at, be, best, big, book, can, cloth, cook, cooking, cried, crust, Dad, desk, dried, exclaimed, fast, felt, for, grandson, grew, grow, handed, he, hike, hiking, him, his, how, in, it, joy, keep, know, like, looked, lot, make, might, Miss, missed, my, not, on, pens, pies, pitches, plate, put, quietly, reading, red, replied, right, Ron, sat, set, she, shouted, smile, so, stopped, stories, teams, telling, that, that's, them, then, things, think, throw, three, threw, Thursday, too, took, try, Tuggle, up, use, went, when, will, with, world, yes, you

High-Frequency Words

Previously Taught
a, already, any, are, could, I, many, now, of, read, said, something, the, thought, to, turnovers, what, you're

Aunt Lizzy Finds Her Cake (p. 33) accompanies *Carousel.*

Decodable Words

New
Sound of *y* at the End of Longer Words: *Benny, Benny's, funny, fuzzy, hurry, Lizzy, messy, Willy*

The Prefix *un-* : *unlike, unlocked, untie, unwise, unwrap*

Previously Taught
and, at, ate, be, big, birthday, box, cake, cakes, can, cars, clue, clues, cookies, cream, day, did, dollars, each, eat, first, flowers, followed, for, forgot, found, get, gift, go, green, had, her, ice, inside, is, it, just, last, lock, look, looked, looking, making, must, need, next, not, note, notes, other, outside, Pam, pen, reads, rushed, she, sleep, slippers, smiled, steps, string, surprise, take, thanks, then, thing, this, time, three, up, urged, waiting, waste, went, white, will, with, writing, you

High-Frequency Words

New
aunt, million, pair

Previously Taught
a, again, are, everyone, find, grow, I, he, in, my, of, read, said, table, the, to, today, was, where, would

My Brother (p. 41) accompanies *Carousel.*

Decodable Words

Review
The *-le* Ending in Two-Syllable Words: apple, bottle, bubbles, bundle, eagle, gentle, giggle, little, rattle, scrambled, settle, table, wiggle, wrinkle

Previously Taught
about, an, and, asks, at, bath, be, bed, best, brother, brothers, can, dad, day, down, eat, eggs, else, for, get, go, hand, he, him, his, home, how, hurry, in, is, Jack, Jack's, last, lets, likes, looks, makes, manners, me, mom, my, name, new, now, or, out, play, playing, quit, read, safe, sees, she, so, splashing, story, talk, teach, tells, thinking, this, three, time, up, walk, walks, we, why, will, with, you

High-Frequency Words

Previously Taught
a, are, does, comes, don't, friends, give, hold, I, I'll, one, table, talk, the, to, two, walk, walks, what, where, your

Eight Daughters! (p. 49) accompanies *Thunder Cake.*

Decodable Words

New
Structural Analysis: Base Words and Endings *-ed, -ing:* bossed, dressed, drumming, filled, getting, skinning

Silent Consonants *gh, kn, b:* bright, daughters, might, night, right, sight, taught, through, tight, knack, kneaded, kneel, knees, knew, know, Knox, limbs

Previously Taught
age, and, at, ate, baked, baking, beat, Bessy, but, came, clothes, crawled, Dad, daugher, did, dinner, Doreen, drums, each, every, everything, face, fact, family, fell, fifteen, five, for, fresh, from, gave, get, good, had, hands, hard, heads, held, her, house, how, hug, in, it, just, Kate, keep, like, liked, little, looked, loud, made, mainly, Meggy, morning, muddy, muffins, Myra, next, not, now,

number, on, patted, Peggy,person, play, played, poor, Sara, scrapes, seven, she, Sissy, sisters, sixth, sleep, smells, smiles, sons, tell, that, them, then, things, time, tree, triplets, tune, very, which, with, yet, you, younger

High-Frequency Words
New
air, child, heavy, hour
Previously Taught
a, about, all, always, around, eight, even, I, neighbors, some, the, their, there, thought, to, was, were

The Family Garden (p. 57) accompanies *Thunder Cake.*

Decodable Words
Review
Sound of *y* at the End of Longer Words: *Daddy, dirty, energy, family, finally, gently, Granny, happy, hurry, many, plenty, seventy, strawberry, sunny, thirsty*
Previously Taught
after, and, Anna, Anna's, baskets, be, best, big, bloom, but, can, cannot, children's, day, days, dinner, each, eat, eats, enjoy, family, food, foods, for, fresh, fun, garden, gardening, get, good, grow, growing, hands, hard, harvest, helps, in, it, make, Mom, more, much, need, nice, now, packed, part, picking, pie, placed, plant, planting, plants, plants', plowing, plows, rows, see, seed, seedlings, seeds, soil, spends, spring, starts, straight, such, sun, surprises, take, takes, tells, that, then, things, this, time, topped, turn, you, weeds, weeks, which, why, with

High-Frequency Words
New
air, heavy
Previously Taught
a, all, are, brother, comes, everyone, her, his, is, long, most, of, pull, sure, the, they, to, water, what, work